Our Folktales

The All-Time Favourite Folktales of Asia

Edited by

Ruth Wan-Lau

Singapore Book Council
Building Our Imagine-nation

WS Education

Published by

WS Education, an imprint of

World Scientific Publishing Co. Pte. Ltd.

5 Toh Tuck Link, Singapore 596224

USA office: 27 Warren Street, Suite 401-402, Hackensack, NJ 07601

UK office: 57 Shelton Street, Covent Garden, London WC2H 9HE

and

In partnership with the Singapore Book Council Ltd
Blk E #03-32 Goodman Arts Centre
90 Goodman Road, Singapore 549043

National Library Board, Singapore Cataloguing in Publication Data
Name(s): Wan, Ruth, 1976– , editor.
Title: Our folktales : the all-time favourite folk tales of Asia / edited by Ruth Wan-Lau.
Description: Singapore : WS Education, [2021]
Identifier(s): OCN 1178912957 | ISBN 978-981-122-634-2 (hardcover) | ISBN 978-981-122-689-2 (paperback)
Subject(s): LCSH: Tales--Asia. | Folklore--Asia.
Classification: DDC 398.2095--dc23

British Library Cataloguing-in-Publication Data
A catalogue record for this book is available from the British Library.

A special thanks to our country-partners and contributors for their unending support of the
Singapore Book Council and AFCC:
CHINA: Ms Wong Swee Yean & Ms Koo Jia Yi
INDIA: Pratham Books & Ms Shabnam Minwalla
INDONESIA: Dr Murti Bunanta & Hardiyono
JAPAN: Mr Tosaku Hatsuyama, Mrs Misa Shirota, Ms Naomi Kojima & Chihiro Art Museum
MALAYSIA: Ms Linda Lingard & Ms Emila Yusof
MYANMAR: Third Story Children's Books & Dr Thant Thaw Kaung
PHILIPPINES: Ms Christine Belen, Ms Frances C Alcaraz, Atty Andrea Pasion-Flores & Anvil Publishing Inc
SINGAPORE: Pustaka Nasional & Ms Eliz Ong
Edited by: Ruth Wan-Lau
The final translations of *Issun-boshi* and *The Princess of Gunung Ledang* were provided by the partner's own translator and editor. The translation of *Issun-boshi* was done by Naomi Kojima, and the translation of *The Princess of Gunung Ledang* was done by Linda Lingard.

Desk editor: Daniele Lee
Design and layout: Jimmy Low

Printed in Singapore

CONTENTS

FOREWORD

The Asian Festival of Children's Content (AFCC) has never fallen short of amazing projects to work on, and this compilation proves yet again the many collaborations that the Festival is capable of inspiring.

What started as a response to a simple call for regional partnership has now blossomed into a special compilation of eight all-time favourite folktales that reflect the diversity that is Asia, and the cohesiveness that is AFCC, both as a festival and as a platform for nurturing traditional and evolving children's content across the region.

This collaborative effort would never have come to print if not for the concerted efforts of the Singapore Book Council (SBC) and the individual partners and contributors from past AFCC Countries of Focus — Ms Wong Swee Yean (China), Pratham Books (India), Dr Murti Bunanta (Indonesia), the Chihiro Art Museum (Japan), Ms Linda Lingard (Malaysia), Dr Thant Thaw Kaung (Myanmar), Atty Andrea Pasion-Flores (Philippines), and Pustaka Nasional (Singapore) — as well as the entire SBC Advisory Network, whose tireless pursuit of bringing children's literature and storytelling to every child in the region is a feat not to be dismissed.

A special thanks to our editorial board comprising publishing luminary Chua Hong Koon; SBC Advisory Network member Evelyn Wong; this collection's editor, children's author Ruth Wan-Lau; and SBC's executive director William Phuan, for providing their invaluable insights in shaping this book into fruition.

As the new norm dawns upon us, we must stand firm alongside each other and not be daunted by the challenges that lie ahead for the literary community. Instead, just as our stories have evolved over time, we must adapt to the changing times ahead, and yet remain true to the core values that our narratives represent — resilience, hope, courage and love.

To you who will open the pages of this compilation, we hope that you will find as much solace and joy as we have had in bringing these countries together through their beloved stories. May you continue to dream of worlds beyond your own, voyaging into the exponential possibilities of the imagination.

Read on!

Claire Chiang

Claire Chiang
Chairperson
Singapore Book Council

PREFACE

In this collection of eight folktales, you will meet brave heroes who outsmart others, mystical spells that enchant, talking animals that are full of mischief, and so much more. The diversity and wonder of Asia are found in these precious tales that have been passed down through generations, and adapted in this compilation for your reading pleasure.

These stories have lasted because they resonate deeply with the cultures they represent. They are not just tales for entertainment (although, they do entertain); they promulgate admirable traits, including strength and determination, family loyalty, love of nature, and even contain hidden allegories that reveal history!

In shortening the text and selecting from original artwork to fit the requirements of this compilation, I have sought to retain the beauty of the stories. I hope you are inspired to read the full versions to enjoy the full flavour of these tales.

It was no small feat pulling together partners and contributors from all over Asia, so, last but not least, I must thank the Singapore Book Council for its tireless efforts to collaborate within Asia and shine the spotlight on the lasting beauty of *Our Folktales*.

Ruth Wan-Lau
Editor
Our Folktales: The All-time Favourite Folktales of Asia

The Zodiac Story

A Chinese folktale

Retold by
Wong Swee Yean

Illustrations by
Koo Jia Yi

A long, long time ago in China, there were no calendars, and people found it hard to remember when they were born or how old they were.

The Jade Emperor, supreme ruler of Heaven and Earth, said, "I will invite all the animals in the kingdom for a great race. The first 12 animals to finish the race will each have a year named after him. This will help the people keep track of their age in 12-year cycles."

Animals of all kinds, big and small, joined the
race. Cat and Rat were best friends who signed
up for the race together. But on the day of the race,
Cat overslept, so Rat started the race without him.

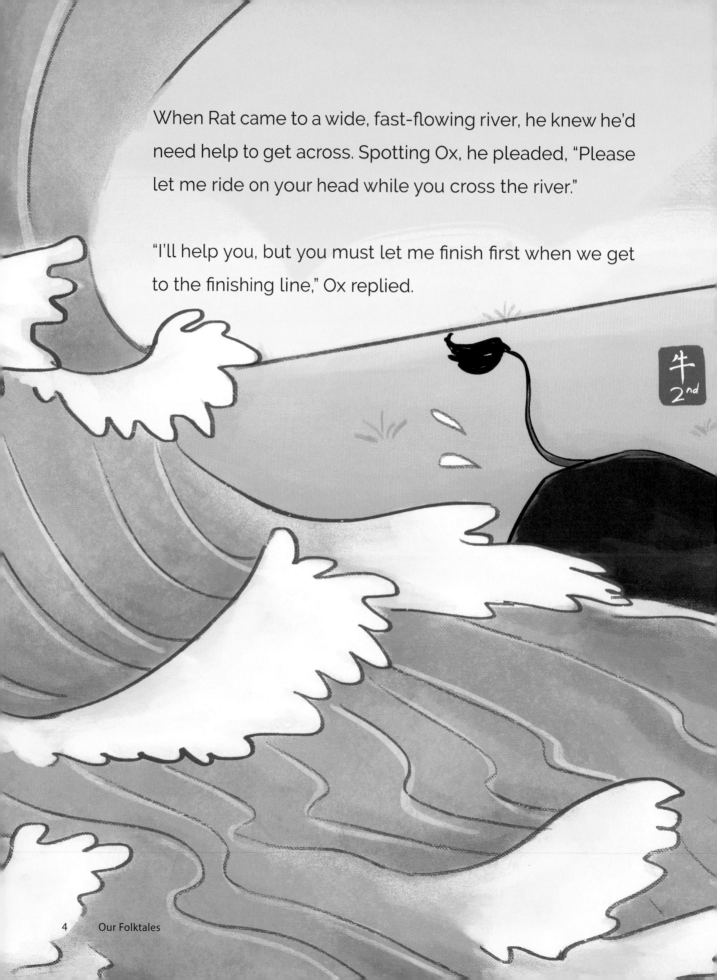

When Rat came to a wide, fast-flowing river, he knew he'd need help to get across. Spotting Ox, he pleaded, "Please let me ride on your head while you cross the river."

"I'll help you, but you must let me finish first when we get to the finishing line," Ox replied.

牛
2nd

Rat agreed, but after they crossed the river together, Rat jumped off Ox's head and sprinted to the finishing line. Rat was first, and Ox could only claim second place.

From behind Ox, there came a roar.
It was Tiger, madly swimming against the strong
current that kept pushing him downstream. When Tiger
discovered he was third in place, he was very angry.

Suddenly, there was a rush of wind. High above, Dragon soared. Below him, Rabbit hopped.

"I can't swim or fly, but I'll hop, hop, hop on the backs of animals and stones, and cross the river to get to the finishing line!" said rabbit, hopping with all his might.

龙
5th

Rabbit came in fourth, and that was a surprise! When Dragon crossed the finishing line, the Jade Emperor asked him why his flying was slower than Rabbit's hopping.

"As I flew above the forest, I saw many people who needed my help. I felt sorry for them, and stopped to help them. That's why I came in fifth," Dragon explained.

While the Jade Emperor was praising Dragon for his compassion, Horse came galloping towards the finishing line.

Snake had been secretly clinging to Horse's leg. "Sssssssssscuse me, Horseeeeee," sneered Snake as he lunged forward at the last moment and crossed the finishing line, claiming sixth place. The startled Horse came in seventh!

Moments later, Sheep, Monkey and Rooster came floating on a log down the river. Sheep steered the log, Monkey flailed his arms like propellers, and Rooster looked out for trouble from behind.

The Jade Emperor was delighted to see the three animals helping one another. Sheep took eight place, Monkey ninth, and Rooster tenth.

"Woof! Woof!" barked Dog, playfully racing to the finishing line. Dog had been enjoying splashing in the water, so the other animals had overtaken him in the race.

猪
12th

狗
11th

And, who was the twelfth animal?

"Oink! Oink!" Pig cried out as he floated in on his round tummy. He had stopped to eat and nap!

"You have arrived just in time to make it to twelfth position," Jade Emperor said, smiling at Pig. "The line-up of twelve animals is now complete."

Just then, Cat arrived at the finishing line.

"Meow! Meow! I'm so sorry I overslept!"
Cat said frantically. Looking at Rat, he added,
"Rat! We are best friends! Why didn't you wake me up on time?"

The Jade Emperor firmly rejected Cat, who stared furiously at Rat standing in first place, before all of the other animals. Cat vowed never to forgive Rat. And so, since that time, cats and rats have been enemies, with cats chasing rats, wherever they are found.

A summary of the folktale

In Chinese culture, a calendar year is marked by an animal from the Chinese zodiac in a repeating cycle of 12 years. How were the 12 animals in the zodiac decided? A great race was declared among all the animals. The race was exciting, with each animal demonstrating unique characteristics and determination to be represented in the zodiac.

More about the folktale

This folktale appeals to young and old because of the many animal characters as well as the exciting race theme. The story is an important aspect of Chinese cultural heritage as it explains why each lunar calendar year is represented by an animal.

For many ethnic Chinese people, the animal sign that they belong to is just as important as their birthdate. They feel proud to bear the personality traits of that animal. As they get older, they may not remember their exact age, but they will certainly remember their zodiac sign and it is not a difficult task to calculate the age of a person based on his zodiac sign. After all, the animal appears in 12-year cycles. There are some ethnic Chinese who take the zodiac more seriously by considering the compatibility of zodiac animals in business partnerships, romance and friendships.

The tale of the Chinese zodiac has been passed down orally in China and around the world. It also has many printed versions and can be found in many languages. In my version, I bring in the unique characteristics of each animal so that listeners will find it easier to remember the sequence of the 12 animals. Koo Jia Yi, who is a tertiary animation student, has done a great job of bringing the tale to life with her vivid illustrations. As a professional storyteller, I will also be publishing a version of this story to commemorate the Federation of Asian Storytellers (FEAST), an annual event where stories are performed in the oral tradition.

This background note was prepared by Wong Swee Yean.

A Camel for Kelam

An Indian folktale

Retold by
Anu Chowdhury-Sorabjee

Illustrations by
Kalyan Joshi

Pabu loved to spend time with animals, and he loved his horse Saffron the most.

Every morning, Pabu brushed Saffron's mane and coat. Then, he saddled Saffron and rode into the desert, far beyond his village in Rajasthan.

Pabu had a niece named Kelam. She loved animals too.

"Pabu," Kelam said. "Bring me a camel for my birthday."

"Where do I find a camel for Kelam?" Pabu wondered.

Camels came from Lanka, which was far, far away, across the big, big sea. Lanka was ruled by a grumpy king who did not share his camels. But Pabu wanted to see a smile on Kelam's face, so he decided to try to get one.

Pabu saddled Saffron and rode all day and all night and all day again, till he saw the vast blue sea for the first time. He and Saffron boarded a boat.

That night, there was a storm so terrible that the winds crashed and the waves lashed. The boat was wrecked. Pabu and Saffron came ashore in a strange place. There were no trees, bees, flowers or rain. Just sand.

Suddenly, Pabu saw camels — many, many camels.

"Hooray," he cried. "I've reached Lanka."

"Welcome," said the king, who was leading the camel riders. Pabu discovered he was in Persia, not Lanka. The happy king invited him to stay in his grand tent.

Pabu spent many days in Persia. He learnt how to groom camels, and also learnt that the grumpy king of Lanka had stolen many of the happy king's camels.

After some weeks, Pabu grew homesick. He wanted to go home with a camel for Kelam.

The happy king gave Pabu a baby camel. He told Pabu to ride across the sand towards the rising sun.

Then, Pabu, Saffron and the baby camel made their way home.

Pabu reached his village just in time for Kelam's birthday. "Kelam, here's a camel for you. Happy birthday!" Pabu said.

The village welcomed Pabu, and Kelam welcomed the baby camel.

And that is how the first camel came to Rajasthan.

A summary of the folktale

Pabu, a Rajasthani chief, loves animals and his niece, Kelam. One day, Kelam tells Pabu that she wants a camel for her birthday, so Pabu sets off to Lanka in search of one. But, after braving a storm, he finds himself in Persia, and befriends the king there. He learns all about camels, and returns with a baby camel for Kelam, just in time for her birthday.

More about the folktale

We decided to develop the story of *A Camel for Kelam* because the artisan is one of the most eminent folk artists in India. The form of painting used in the book is Phad painting and Kalyan Joshi is the 30th generation artisan to practice this art form which is slowly disappearing. A Camel for Kelam was originally published by Pratham Books in 2019.

Even today, in Rajasthan, children grow up listening to the stories of local folk heroes, like Pabuji and Devnarayan, from family and wandering minstrels. In Rajasthan, large horizontal paintings called Phad paintings portray the epic lives of local folk heroes and demi-gods and form a visual backdrop to all-night storytelling performances. The performer's assistant illuminates parts of the painting with an oil lamp, as the performer recounts the story with song and dance to the accompaniment of instruments.

The story *A Camel for Kelam* is based on one of the two main Rajasathani folk epics, the Epic of Pabuji. In the original story, Pabuji was a 14th-century Rathor prince, born from a celestial nymph who promised to return to him in the form of a mare when he was 12. One of Pabuji's early exploits was to fight the Khici clan, which had encroached on his country's borders and was treating him and his brother arrogantly. He acquired a black mare from Lady Deval of the Caran clan. The mare, of course, was his mother. Pabuji overthrew Mirza Khan, arranged for the marriage of his niece, and stole a herd of she-camels from Lanka (Lanka here does not refer to the island, but symbolically to a kingdom west of the Indus river) for his niece Kelam.

This background note was prepared by Pratham Books.

Princess Kemang

An Indonesian folktale from Bengkulu province

Retold by **Murti Bunanta**

Illustrations by **Hardiyono**

Princess Kemang was an adventurous young warrior who loved to hunt, fish and hike in the woods. One day, when she was hunting, she spotted a striped-leg deer. She shot her arrow quickly, but missed.

Startled, the deer ran deep into the woods, with Princess Kemang chasing right behind it.

Suddenly, the deer stopped under a kemang tree.

"Dear princess, don't chase after this deer. It is actually a tiger in disguise," said the tree.

Princess Kemang was startled to hear the kemang tree giving her advice, but, determined to kill the deer, she shot her arrow straight through its body. Instantly, the deer died and transformed into a tiger.

Then, something even stranger happened. The kemang tree changed into a handsome young man.

"I am the guardian of this forest," said the man. "I can't leave the forest until everything in it has changed to human form and the forest has turned into a kingdom."

"If the forest becomes a kingdom, I will return for you," the princess replied. "I want to be your friend."

Then, she continued hunting, walking from one forest to another, from one meadow to another, and from one hill to another.

When Princess Kemang finally decided to go back home, she came to a river infested with hungry crocodiles.

"Princess, you will be our meal," the biggest crocodile said to her.

"Oh, I can fight a thousand crocodiles by myself," the princess replied. "Call all your friends here, and line up, so I can count you. I want to make sure there are really one thousand of you, before the battle begins."

The crocodiles came and formed a line. The princess jumped on each of their backs, counting them as she went. In that way, she crossed the wide river.

How angry the crocodiles were when they realised that they had been tricked!

A year later, Princess Kemang was out hunting when she found herself in a huge forest.

She walked along a long river there and after three days, she was surprised to see a kingdom in a forest.

As Princess Kemang approached the kingdom, she saw an old man. "What is the name of this kingdom?" Princess Kemang asked him. "And, who is the king?"

The old man replied: "This is Kemang kingdom. Prince Kemang is the king. Before, this was known as a ghost forest because it was occupied by supernatural spirits. Prince Kemang was a god who had been cursed and turned into a kemang tree. However, the curse would be broken if a human spoke to the tree. Then, the tree could become human and the forest could become a kingdom."

Princess Kemang realised Prince Kemang was the guardian of the forest she had met a year ago. She asked the old man to take her to see him.

Prince Kemang recognised Princess Kemang. He accepted her invitation to visit her kingdom.

The prince and princess travelled together. Before the dawn on the fifth day, they arrived at the kingdom of Princess Kemang.

The King approached them with happiness, welcoming the prince with food and drinks. He was surprised to hear the prince's story and asked him to become his son-in-law.

The servants were commanded to prepare a royal wedding party. The celebrations lasted seven days and seven nights.

When the king became old, he gave his throne to his daughter, Princess Kemang.

The two kingdoms were united. Princess Kemang and Prince Kemang lived happily ever after.

A summary of the folktale

For many centuries, Indonesian folktales have taught the equality of women and men. The story of Princess Kemang from Bengkulu Province in Sumatra Island is about an independent princess who, fond of hunting, fishing and hiking in the woods, eventually becomes a soldier. Once, in a dense forest, she spoke to a tree which then changed slowly into a handsome prince. Later, the two married and Princess Kemang became the ruler of her kingdom.

More about the folktale

The idea to choose a folktale from my books as the representative of Indonesia was brought up by one of the editors who is very familiar with Indonesian children's books and knowledgeable about the quality of the books published by Kelompok Pencinta Bacaan Anak.

Based on this suggestion and encouragement, I decided to choose a story from the books I had written. The story of Princess Kemang has been published in the US and Canada in English, and has been translated into Mongolian and German. This is a relevant story for current and future generations everywhere to learn about the equality of women and men.

The source of this story comes from a documentation project from oral retelling, *Folktales from Bengkulu* published by the Department of Education and Culture, Inventory and Documentation of Regional Culture Project, Jakarta, 1982.

This background note was prepared by Dr Murti Bunanta.

ISSUN-boshi

A Japanese folktale

Retelling and illustrations by

Shigeru Hatsuyama

むかしむかしの

神さまに
神さまに

爺と媼とが
子をもろた。

豆つぶこつぶな
子をもろた

ものがたり

一寸法師。

A long, long time ago, God gave an old man and his old wife a gift.

God gave them a child, a tiny child, and they named him Issun-boshi.

"Issun-boshi is a cry baby," teased the children.

"Make him cry!"

"Here comes the lord's horse. Walk through the horse's legs, you little bean!" they jeered.

おとほりだ
またくゞれ。

一寸法師の

なきむしぼうし

いぢめろ

なかせ。

豆つぶぼうし。

殿様おうまの

ひとりぼっちで
たびにでた。

なきむし法師は
ひとりぼうし

爺からおいとま

わんもろて

One day, Issun-boshi bade farewell to the old man and said goodbye to the old woman.

The old man gave him a wooden bowl. The old woman gave him a chopstick.

He was off to see the world.

Issun-boshi, the cry baby, was now on his own.

よどの
かはせを

わんぶらこ

ぎっちらこ。

おわんのおふね
わんぶらこ

Bobbing along the riverbank and steering the bowl with his chopstick, Issun-boshi went down the Yodo river.

Oh, the Capital was huge.

Tiny Issun-boshi set out to find a job in the big city.

都はみやこ
でっかいぞ
つぶはちひさい法師でも

でっかい都で

あすは

熊野へおともする

御主人だいじに

おともする。

おともする

おひめさまの

おともする

清水さまへ

Issun-boshi guarded the princess on her outing to Kiyomizu Temple.

Tomorrow he would accompany her to Kumano Shrine.

It was his job to take good care of the princess.

"Ogres! Stop laughing.
You'll be sorry," shouted Issun-boshi.

"I may be small but see my needle
sword.

Go away before I sting you."

こら鬼め！
わらふなよ
ちびはちびだが
みえるだろ。

針のかたなも
みえる
だろ

まごまご
すると

"Ouch, Ouch. Stop it, you brat," cried the ogres.

"No more, I'm sorry. Ouch, oh ouch!"

The ogres fled and left their magic mallet behind.

The princess waved the mallet and she sang,

"Grow tall, Issun-boshi, grow taller than the mountains."

With each wave he grew taller and taller.

Issun-boshi was now a fine young man, standing tall in the big city.

一寸法師の
せいのびろ

鬼のわすれた

うちでの
こづち

こっこっこっりこ。

山よりたかく

せいせいのびろ。

豆つぶぼうしは
りっぱこりって

A summary of the folktale

Issun-boshi is a tiny boy, no taller than one *sun* (3 cm), but he is brave and spirited. With a needle as a sword, he rides down the river in a wooden bowl to find work in the capital. A lord hires him to guard his daughter, the princess. During an outing, the princess is attacked by ogres and Issun-boshi saves her. The ogres leave a mallet behind. The mallet is magical and it changes Issun-boshi's life forever.

More about the folktale

The original version of this picture book was published in 1929 at a time when modern Japanese picture books were emerging. The story itself is from the 14th century and is still loved in Japan today. The East and West have many stories of adventurous small protagonists no larger than a thumb; we thought this familiar story would delight readers around the world. The illustrations are by Shigeru Hatsuyama, an artist who was active in children's books and woodblock prints from the 1920s to the early 1970s. His style is reminiscent of Japanese modernism while his illustrations continue to captivate readers after 90 years. We believe picture books are cultural assets; they are entities that transcend time and bring everlasting joy to children and adults. This book is one of such entities, a symbol of our hope for picture books.

This background note was prepared by the Chihiro Art Museum.

The Princess of Gunung Ledang

A Malaysian folktale

Retelling and illustrations
by **Emila Yusof**

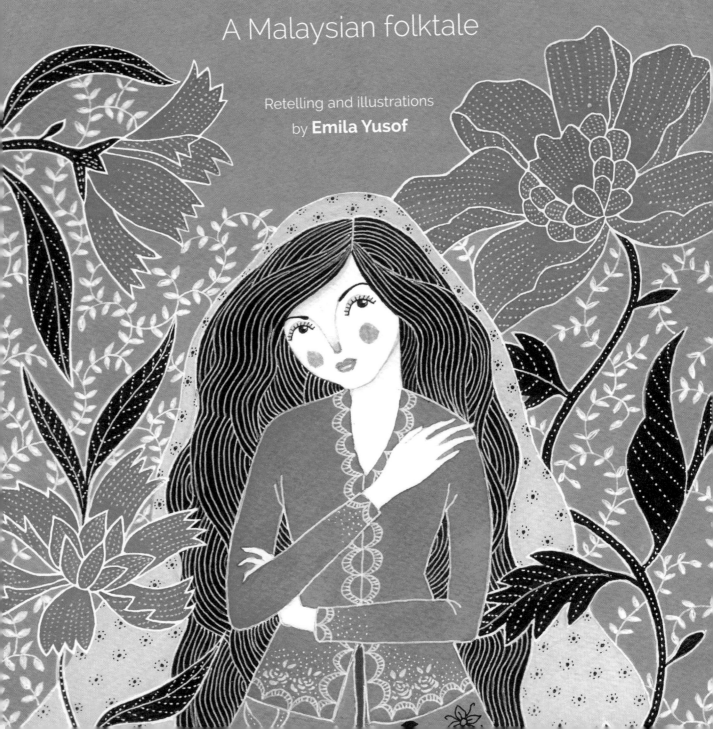

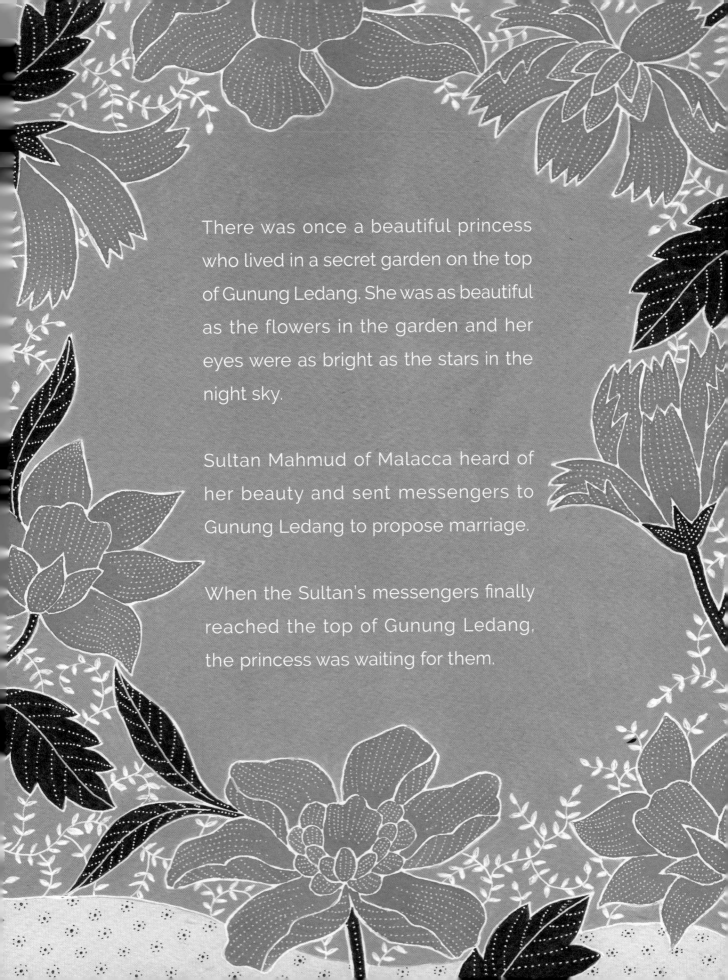

There was once a beautiful princess who lived in a secret garden on the top of Gunung Ledang. She was as beautiful as the flowers in the garden and her eyes were as bright as the stars in the night sky.

Sultan Mahmud of Malacca heard of her beauty and sent messengers to Gunung Ledang to propose marriage.

When the Sultan's messengers finally reached the top of Gunung Ledang, the princess was waiting for them.

"I accept the Sultan's marriage proposal on the condition he fulfils seven wishes," she said.

"First, build me a bridge of gold from Gunung Ledang to Malacca and second, build me a silver bridge from Malacca to Gunung Ledang."

Eager to prove his love, the Sultan began building and in no time the two bridges were built.

"Now I wish for seven trays of gnat hearts and seven trays of mosquito hearts," said the princess.

The Sultan's messengers gasped when they heard this but the Sultan ordered that the Princess's third and fourth wishes be fulfilled immediately.

And so it was done.

When the trays were delivered to her, the Princess only said, "Seven barrels of maidens' tears, no more, no less, is my fifth wish."

"Gather all the maidens in Malacca and order them to cry until their tears fill seven barrels," commanded the Sultan.

And so it was done.

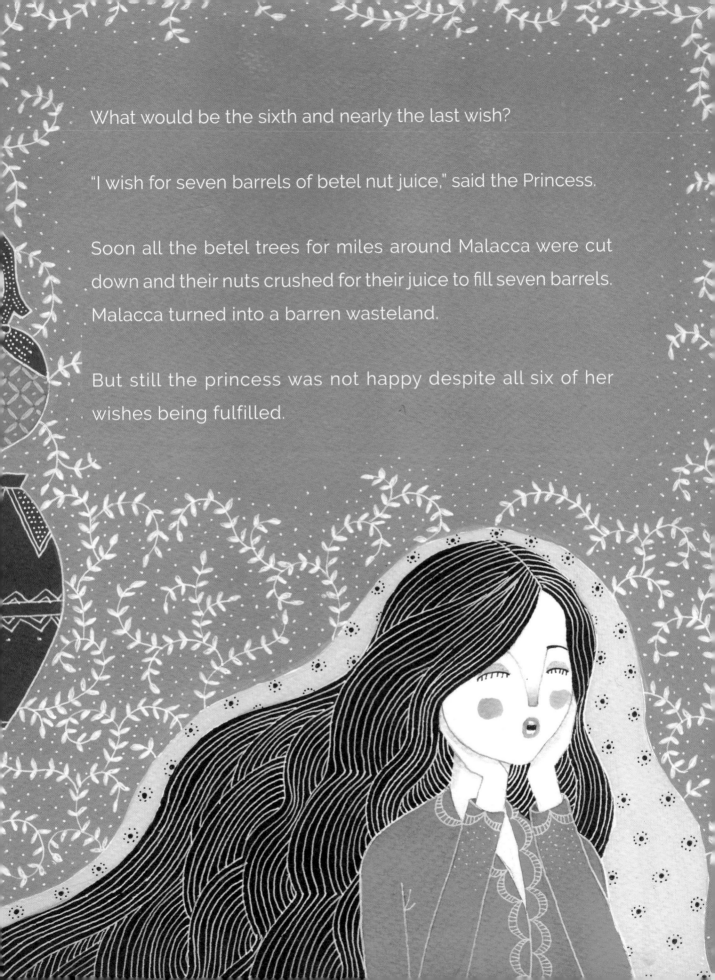

What would be the sixth and nearly the last wish?

"I wish for seven barrels of betel nut juice," said the Princess.

Soon all the betel trees for miles around Malacca were cut down and their nuts crushed for their juice to fill seven barrels. Malacca turned into a barren wasteland.

But still the princess was not happy despite all six of her wishes being fulfilled.

She smiled coldly and said, "My last and seventh wish is for a bowl of blood — the blood of the Sultan's son."

When the Sultan heard this, he was horrified. He was not prepared to risk his son's life.

So he withdrew his offer of marriage.

Did the Princess of Gunung Ledang really want to marry the Sultan? Were her wishes to test the Sultan's love or a ruse to reject his proposal?

The Princess of Gunung Ledang is as beautiful as she is mysterious. As far as we know, she still lives in her secret garden on the top of Gunung Ledang.

A summary of the folktale

The beautiful Princess of Gunung Ledang lived happily on the top of the mountain, Ledang. When the powerful Sultan of Melaka came courting, the princess had to think of a way to reject his proposal. She came up with dowry requests that she felt sure the Sultan would not be able to fulfil. Alas, the Sultan fulfilled all six requests and was ready to claim his prize when the princess came up with a seventh request: a bowl of the royal prince's blood.

More about the folktale

The legend of Puteri Gunung Ledang (Princess of Gunung Ledang) was first recorded in *Sulalatus Salatin* (Genealogy of Kings), a historical work of literature of the Malay Sultanate in the 15th and early 16th century. Better known as the *Malay Annals* or *Sejarah Melayu* today, it was originally written in Classical Malay in old Jawi script. The manuscript has been rewritten and translated, and it can be found in libraries around the world, including Malaysia, Singapore, Indonesia, UK, and the Netherlands.

In 2001, the *Malay Annals* was listed in UNESCO's Memory of the World Programme International Register, in recognition of the need to preserve this precious piece of heritage. The legend of Puteri Gunung Ledang has been adapted into films and produced as a stage musical.

This background note was prepared by Linda Lingard.

Journey to Happy Land

A Myanmarese folktale

Retold by
Thor Zin Htut Aung

Illustrations by
Edo Vader

Pu Lone, an egg-shaped toy with a brightly painted face, was leading his friends to Happy Land. It was a difficult and dangerous journey, and his friends were tired.

To stay motivated, Pu Lone and his friends sang a song:

"Oh, Happy Land, Happy Land,
here we come. Arm in arm,
we are travelling to our Happy Land!"

Soon, Pu Lone and his friends met Skinny Cat. "You'll never get to Happy Land," Skinny Cat told them. "There are many toys that will get there before you and they will not let you in."

Pho Wa Yote, the ever-curious chubby boy who wore a gold medallion necklace, followed Skinny Cat further down the path to take a look. The next day, he returned all wet.

"Skinny Cat took me to spy on the other toys making their way to Happy Land. They looked so different from us!" Pho Wa Yote told his friends.

"When the toys saw me, they shouted, 'Get that fatty!' and they chased after me. While I was running away, I fell into a river, so now I am spoilt." Pho Wa Yote was made of paper.

Chinlone Nga Nyo, the woven rattan ball, said, "What terrible toys! We must fight back!"

Nwa Gyi, the cow who always felt a little nervous, softly cried, "Don't we deserve to live in Happy Land?"

Pu Lone replied: "Of course we do! Don't be discouraged." He urged everyone to stay calm.

Pu Lone and his friends sang:

"Happy Land, Happy Land, here we come. We must be Brave and claim our land!"

They saw the modern toys coming their way.

Chinlone Nga Nyo rolled over the police car that was coming at them. The doll with long hair pushed Nwa Gyi over. A giant robot, Robot Ta Ti, ran straight at Pho Wa Yote and Pu Lone.

Robot Ta Ti threw Pu Lone down but since Pu Lone was shaped like an egg, he bounced right back up. As they fought, they both fell into the water. Neither could swim.

Suddenly, Pu Lone and Robot Ta Ti washed up on shore in a beautiful place full of flowers. They had reached Happy Land!

Pu Lone asked, "Why are you strange toys attacking us?"

Robot Ta Ti answered, "We were told that an enemy was coming to attack us and wouldn't allow us to enter Happy Land."

"Pho Wa Yote was not going to attack you," explained Pu Lone. "We only attacked you because you attacked him."

Now, they understood that they had all been tricked! The one who had started the conflict was Skinny Cat!
Pu Lone and Robot Ta Ti went back to explain everything to their friends.

A few days later, all the toys
arrived at Happy Land.
There were many children
there who loved all of them.

The toys loved to hear the sound of the children laughing and playing. The traditional toys, Pu Lone and his friends, made peace with the modern toys, and everyone sang together:

"Happy Land, Happy Land, here we are. Arm in arm, we live in Happy Land."

A summary of the folktale

This is a story about displaced toys searching for a place to live happily and safely, away from the war zone. During their journey, they meet a cat who warns them that some toys will try to prevent these traditional toys from entering Happy Land. So, the displaced traditional toys have to fight to enter Happy Land.

More about the folktale

In this folktale, Pu Lone is a *pyit taing htaung*, a traditional Myanmarese toy made of paper. Each time a pyit taing htaung is thrown or pushed down, it stands back up, thus symbolising resilience, perseverance and the ability to overcome defeat. Pu Lone's friends, Pho Wa Yote, Chinlone Nga Nyo and Nwa Gyi, are all traditional Myanmarese toys too.

The author of this story aims to promote the value and importance of peace. We chose this story to be included in this book for three reasons: Firstly, traditional toys are in danger of being forgotten by our Myanmarese children. We want to give prominence to these toys as they should be remembered and conserved. Secondly, this story brings across a relevant message for today's generation. It is vital not to believe everything you hear, but to always check whether information is based on facts by checking the source. This is something important for all Myanmarese today. Finally, we believe that every child has the right to be protected and to live happily. All children deserve a place in Happy Land.

It is our hope that through this story, readers will come to learn of the important values and ideals for not only our Myanmarese children, but for children everywhere in the world.

This background note was prepared by Third Story Books.

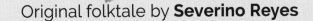

Original folktale by **Severino Reyes**

The Brother of the Three Marias

A Philippine folktale

Retold by
Christine S. Bellen

Illustrations by
Frances C. Alcaraz

Teong and Goya were healers who lived at the foot of Monte Sagrado. Their daughters, Maria Upeng, Maria Loleng and Maria Trining, picked the leaves of the Kolesmeloko tree every morning because its leaves could heal any illness.

One day, when Teong cut down the tree to pick all of its leaves, a huge snake emerged. It had been imprisoned in the tree by the King of the Lions, the King of the Eagles, and the King of the Sharks.

"Thank you for freeing me," said the snake. "But now, your three daughters will have to take my place."

Teong went home to tell his family. Goya was devastated, but the three brave daughters made up their minds to go with the snake.

The next morning, the three Marias went to the tree, and disappeared. The snake told Teong not to worry as they were going to become the wives of the three kings. In exchange, Teong and Goya were given five gold coins.

Soon, Goya gave birth to a son named Pedro. She always sung him songs about the three Marias and how they disappeared, so when he grew up, he decided to look for his sisters.

Goya gave him the five gold coins and three handkerchiefs that had his sisters' names on them.

During his journey, Pedro met three men who had received gifts from an old beggar — a hat that made you invisible, a key that could open any door, and sandals that could make you fly.

Pedro offered to buy these gifts with his five gold coins. The three men agreed.

Wearing the hat, Pedro commanded the sandals to bring him to the Kingdom of the Sharks. Using the key, he reached the throne of King Urano, and removed his hat and bowed.

"I am Pedro, Maria Trining's brother," Pedro said.

"But, I do not have a brother," said the Queen.

Pedro showed her the handkerchief with her name on it. The King gave Pedro a pearl as big as a chicken's egg for Teong and Goya, and promised to bring the Queen to visit them soon.

Pedro flew to the Kingdom of the Eagles. Using the key, he reached the throne of King Langay, and removed his hat and bowed.

"I am Pedro, Maria Loleng's brother," Pedro said.

"But, I do not have a brother," said the Queen.

Pedro showed her the handkerchief with her name on it. The King gave Pedro the finest gold and silver carved with birds for Teong and Goya, and promised to bring the Queen to visit them soon.

Pedro then travelled to the Kingdom of the Lions. Using the key, he reached the throne of King Araw, and removed his hat and bowed for the third time.

"I am Pedro, Maria Upeng's brother," Pedro said.

"But, I do not have a brother," said the Queen.

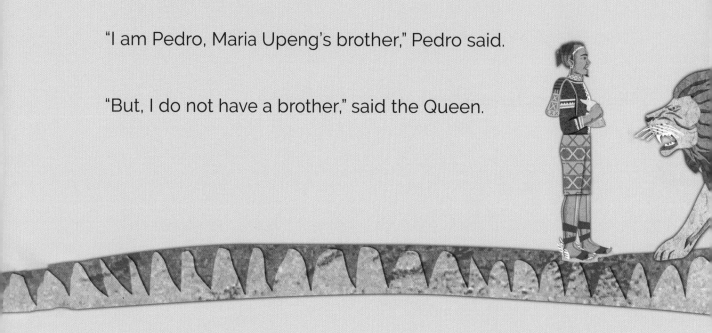

Pedro showed her the handkerchief with her name on it. The King gave Pedro a necklace made of diamonds for Teong and Goya, and promised to bring the Queen to visit them soon.

Pedro returned home and gave Teong and Goya the gifts.

Suddenly, King Urano and Queen Maria Trining arrived from the sea on a golden chariot pulled by whales, King Langay and Queen Maria Loleng arrived on a giant bird with glittering feathers, and King Araw and Queen Maria Upeng arrived on two huge lions.

The family was reunited at last. From that day on, Pedro was known as "the Brother of the Three Marias".

A summary of the folktale

After cutting down a magical kolesmeloko tree for profit, Teong the folk healer, accidentally sets a giant serpent free. As punishment for his greed he must give away his three daughters, Maria Upeng, Maria Loleng, and Maria Upeng, to three powerful kings. Many years pass and the youngest child, Pedro, journeys across different realms in an effort to find his sisters and reunite his family.

More about the folktale

When asked to submit a story to represent the Philippines in this collection, we immediately thought of the Lola Basyang Story Collection written by Severino Reyes and retold by Christine Bellen. Lola Basyang, an enduring figure of storytelling in Philippine Children's literature, is a source of stories filled with lessons and whimsical characters. To choose a suitable tale, we took into account which story conveyed the values of Philippine culture the best. When it came to *The Brother of the Three Marias*, this story was chosen for its depiction of how Filipinos place great importance on family, as well as the colourful illustrations inspired by the people of Mindanao.

The original text of the story was written by Severino Reyes for *Liwayway*, the literary magazine of its day. After watching children gather at the feet of Gervasia Guzman de Zamora or "Tandang Basiang" to hear stories at Zamora House during dinner parties, Reyes became inspired to make children's stories of his own under the pen name, Lola Basyang. It was Reyes' aim to take the western fairy tale format and repackage it for a Filipino audience while imbuing each story with lessons that resonate with our values. For this story, the text was retold by Christine Bellen, who, together with the colourful illustrations of Frances Alcaraz, was able to capture the original charm of the story.

This background note was prepared by Anvil Publishing.

BADANG
THE MIGHTY WARRIOR
A Singaporean folktale

Retold by
Abdullah Basmeh
Illustrations by **Eliz Ong**

Badang was a slave who lived in Seluang. Weak and poor, Badang had to find food for himself. Every morning he would set fish traps in the river.

One day, he found his fish traps empty except for fish scales and bones. This happened for a few days. "Who has been stealing my fish?" wondered Badang. The next day, determined to get to the bottom of this mystery, he hid behind some reeds to try to catch the thief.

When a demon with fiery red eyes appeared and greedily ate the fish caught in the traps, Badang took out his cleaver and charged at him.

"Don't kill me! I will give you whatever you want!" the demon pleaded.

Knowing his master would take any wealth away from him, he asked the demon for great strength so he could finish all of the tasks his master set for him.

"Very well," said the demon. "But first, you have to swallow my vomit."

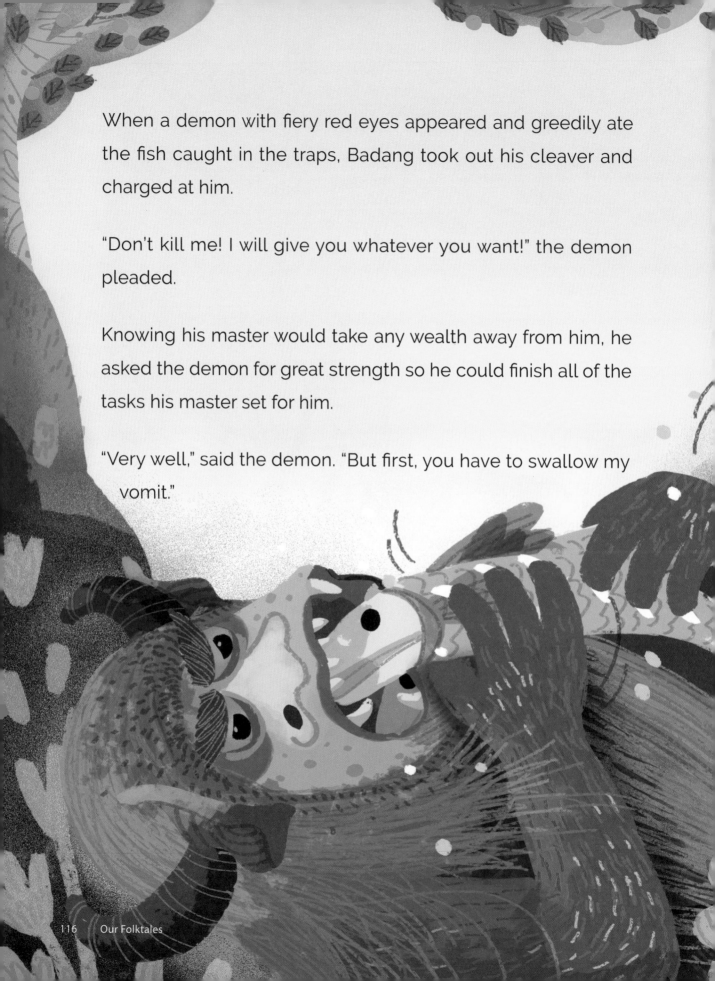

The demon vomited a great amount, and Badang swallowed it all. He gained so much strength that he could uproot huge trees and clear land for his master rapidly. Badang's master was overjoyed.

To thank Badang, he said: "From this day on, you are no longer my slave."

News of Badang's amazing strength began to spread. When the Raja of Singapura heard of it, he summoned Badang to the palace.

The Raja had ordered his people to build a perahu within the palace grounds. This boat measured fifteen arm spans in length and it was so heavy, not even three thousand people could move it.

"Can you help me?" the Raja asked Badang.

"I will move the boat for you," Badang replied. Using his muscular arms and legs, he pushed the boat all the way from the palace to the sea, by himself!

The king was amazed at Badang's strength and made him a royal warrior.

Soon, the King of India heard that the Raja of Singapura had a mighty warrior named Badang.

He ordered his strongest warrior Nadi Bijaya Pikrama to challenge him.

"Sail to Singapura and wrestle with Badang," the king told his warrior. "If you lose, I will give the Raja of Singapura seven shiploads of goods. But, if Badang loses, I will demand seven shiploads of goods from him!"

Thousands of people came to watch the wrestling match between Badang and Nadi Bijaya Pikrama. The two men were locked in each other's arms in fierce combat. Each fought his very best. But ultimately, Badang emerged victorious.

Feeling ashamed, Nadi Bijaya Pikrama suggested one final challenge. "Let us demonstrate our strength by lifting that boulder," he said, pointing to a gigantic rock near the wrestling ring. "Whoever is unable to lift it will be the loser."

Nadi Bijaya Pikrama used all of his might and managed to lift the boulder up to his knees. But, Badang easily lifted the boulder over his head. With a smile, he flung it all the way to Kuala Singapura, the estuary of the Singapore River.

Hence, the warrior of India had to surrender seven ships and their precious cargo to Badang. And, the fame of Badang continued to spread like wildfire.

Over the years, more powerful warriors came to challenge Badang, but none of them could defeat the warrior of Singapura who possessed tremendous strength. Badang remained the undefeated hero of Singapura, defending his King and country's honour for as long as he lived!

A summary of the folktale

Badang, a poor labourer, uses his wits to gain super strength and freedom from his master. The Raja of Singapura hears reports about this strongman, and summons Badang to his kingdom. With his quick mind and strength, Badang becomes legendary as the undefeatable royal warrior, defending his King and country's honour. Among his many challenges, Badang lifts a gigantic boulder, and hurls it to the mouth of the Singapore River.

More about the folktale

The story of Badang is among the tales of Singapore legends found in the literary work, *Sejarah Melayu*, or *Malay Annals*. The earliest version of these records, Sulalatus Salatin (Genealogy of Kings), was written in classical Malay in Jawi script in the 15th–16th century. Pustaka Nasional published the story of Badang as *Hulubalang Gagah* in 1963. It was part of a Malay Fables Series for young readers to appreciate selected narrations from the Malay Annals. The series was edited by Abdullah Basmeh with illustrations by the late S Mohdir (Haji Mohamed Haji Adbul). The English translation, *The Mighty Warrior*, was published in 2015.

The story of Badang continues to be a favourite folktale among storytellers in Singapore today. Children are delighted by the adventures of a Singapore superhero who had extraordinary powers. They can also relate the story to one of Singapore's national treasures, the Singapore Stone, that is on display at our National Museum. The Singapore Stone is a fragment of a large slab dating back to the 13th century or earlier, that was blown up to clear the way in the Singapore River in 1843. It is believed to have come from the boulder that Badang hurled into the Singapore River in the days of rajas and warriors.

This background note was prepared by Evelyn Sue Wong.